The Holly Story Book Library

The Holly Story Book Library

The Holly Story Book Library

The Holly Story Book Library

The Holly Story Book Library

The Holly Story Book Library

The Holly Story Book Library

The Holly Story Book Library

The Holly Story Book Library

The Holly Story Book Library

THE VIKINGS

THE VIKINGS

By
Barbara Selfridge

General Editor
M. Hughes Miller
Former Publications Director,
and Founder of Weekly
Reader Children's Book Club

Editorial Director
Josephine B. Wolfe
Director Language Arts
Research, Beaver College;
Former Director Reading
Research, State Department,
Pennsylvania, and Former
Assistant Managing Editor of
My Weekly Reader.

Illustrated by
Riera Rojas

The Holly Story Book Library
THE WORLD PUBLISHING COMPANY
CLEVELAND AND NEW YORK

THE VIKINGS

A Holly Book

Published by The World Publishing Company

2231 West 110th Street, Cleveland, Ohio 44102

Published simultaneously in Canada by Nelson, Foster & Scott Ltd.

First Holly Printing 1965

Library of Congress Catalog Card Number: 65-24740

Printed in the United States of America

THE HOLLY STORY BOOK LIBRARY both attracts and holds young readers. Each title is illustrated in exciting full color; each is either translated or edited by well-known and respected writers and educators.

General Editor

M. HUGHES MILLER

Former Publications Director, and Founder of
Weekly Reader Children's Book Club

Editorial Director

JOSEPHINE B. WOLFE

Director of Language Arts Research, Beaver College;
Former Director of Reading Research, State Department, Pennsylvania,
and Former Assistant Managing Editor of My Weekly Reader.

Associate Editors and Authors

MARGUERITE R. DUFFY, B.A., M.A.   DORIS R. MILLER B.A.
MURIEL W. ROTHBERG, B.A., M.A.   KATHRYN FRENCH, B.A.
EVE ROUKE, B.A., M.A.   BARBARA SELFRIDGE, B.A., M.A.

Designer

HELGA MAASS

Illustrator

RIERA ROJAS

THE VIKINGS

More than twelve hundred years ago people known as the Vikings lived in the lands now called Norway, Denmark, and Sweden. They were cruel, warlike people. During the 700's they began to attack the countries of Western Europe. Soon all of Europe lived in fear of the Vikings. These warriors came from the northern seas to burn cities, steal valuables, and kill everyone who stood in

their way. Every Sunday the people of Europe prayed in their churches, asking God for help against these frightening Vikings. But it was of no use! Again and again the Vikings came in their strange ships, bringing death and destruction with them.

Usually, the Vikings gave no warning that they were going to attack. They would cross the Northern Seas quickly and quietly in their long, narrow ships. These ships had high pointed fronts which were shaped like the head of a horse or the head of a dragon. Because of this, the ships were called "dragons." Every dragon carried one big square sail. On each side of the dragon there was usually a row of fifteen oars.

With so many oars and such a big sail, the ships could travel in all kinds of weather. This made the Northmen "Kings of the Sea."

Several dragons in a group would usually sail together to raid a country. When the Vikings reached the coast of a land they were going to attack, they would hide their ships. Then they would go quickly on foot to the nearest village. Before anyone knew what was happening, the Vikings would attack the town from all sides. Some would shoot bows and arrows. Others would attack with swords. Most of the Vikings carried heavy battle-axes which had long handles. In a single blow a Viking could rip a metal shield in two, or cut off a head, an arm, or a leg. Sometimes, a Viking could even knock down a horse with his battle-ax. Because the Vikings were very smart, they learned to use the things they found in other countries. These all helped them in battle. At first they had only round shields to protect themselves. Soon, however, the Vikings learned to use pointed metal helmets and coats made of iron. This new armor, they found, gave them more protection for their heads and bodies. Therefore, the Viking warriors were not so badly wounded in battle. They learned this from the people they fought. Although they had never seen horses before, they quickly learned how to use them in fighting.

In most cases it did not take the Vikings very long to win a battle. The people of the village defended themselves as best they could. However, they did not have much chance against the strength and surprise attacks of the Vikings. Afterward, when a battle was over and the town was burned, the Vikings would sail away as quickly as they had come.

Today, the actions of the Vikings seem cruel to us, but in those days life was very different. People's ideas of what was good and what was bad were not the same as ours are today. Many men did very cruel things to each other. The Vikings believed that it was good to be warlike, to attack and to rob. Their religion taught them that the best life was that of a soldier. Their most important god was a warrior named Odin. It was said that he rode across the sky on a white horse carrying a large sword in his hand. It was also said that Odin lived in Asgard, not far from a place called Valhalla.

Valhalla was the Vikings' heaven. It was supposed to be a huge palace built in the middle of the sky. It was believed that the palace was made of shining gold. Valhalla had 550 doors. These doors were so large that a single row of eight men could go out of one door at the same time. Of course, every Viking wanted to go to Valhalla. But Odin wanted only the souls of men who had died bravely in battle to join him. Therefore, every Viking fought very hard and bravely. Each one hoped to be allowed to join Odin. Each one hoped to have a soul brave enough to go to Valhalla.

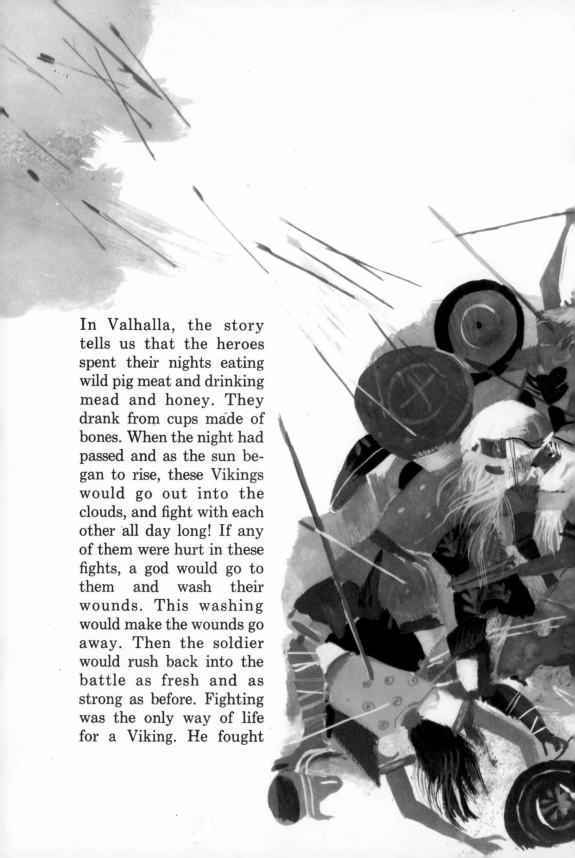

In Valhalla, the story tells us that the heroes spent their nights eating wild pig meat and drinking mead and honey. They drank from cups made of bones. When the night had passed and as the sun began to rise, these Vikings would go out into the clouds, and fight with each other all day long! If any of them were hurt in these fights, a god would go to them and wash their wounds. This washing would make the wounds go away. Then the soldier would rush back into the battle as fresh and as strong as before. Fighting was the only way of life for a Viking. He fought

during all the years he was on earth. He fought fiercely because he was not afraid to die. For him, dying was not the end of a battle. It was the beginning of the best fight of all. They would continue fighting in heaven!

The Vikings sailed from the north to attack the countries of Europe for more than 150 years. They sailed to France, Germany England, Scotland, and Spain. In France the Vikings were the most successful. There, many of the people lived on farms, so their houses were spread over the countryside. Therefore the people had no way to protect themselves from the Vikings. Even the cities could not protect themselves too well because they were so small. Often there was no more than a simple wood or stone fence around a city. This was not enough to keep the Vikings out. Unfortunately, it was the churches and monasteries of France that had the worst time. They too were unprotected.

So naturally the Vikings liked to attack them even more than any other place. The churches and monasteries had many treasures in them. Here the raiders found gold cups, statues, cloths of silk, and other rich treasures.

As the years went by, even the big cities in France were not safe from the attacks of the Vikings. Paris was attacked at three different times. Twice the Vikings set fire to the city. The people of Paris fought bravely against the Vikings, but in the end the King of France had to give the Vikings many silver coins. Only then, did they promise that they would leave the city alone.

After the third attack on Paris, not all of the Vikings left France to return home. By the end of the eight hundreds many of the Vikings were still in France. They decided that it would be a good idea to live in the warm, rich countries of Europe. So, instead of returning to their homelands, they stayed on. Their own countries were cold and crowded with people.

Many of the Vikings built camps in the countries which they attacked. One man who stayed was named Roland. He was so tall that no horse could be found that was big enough for him! So he always went everywhere on foot. Soon everyone called him the Wanderer.

Roland, the Wanderer, and his group of men settled down on the Seine River, not far from Paris, in a place called Rouen. Soon the people of Rouen learned that the Vikings did not plan to return to their own country. But they could not drive the Vikings out. So, to protect themselves, they tried to make some agreements with the Vikings. After much talking it was agreed that the Northmen (who became known as Norsemen) would move into the city of Rouen, help build walls around it, and live in peace with the people of Rouen. The Vikings did as they promised. But they also went out from Rouen and attacked the people and lands nearby. These attacks caused a great deal of alarm. Finally, Charles, the king of France, was able to make peace with Roland. He promised the Viking leader that he would make him a Duke and give him a great deal of French land. He also told Roland that he would give him his daughter in marriage. In return, Roland promised to become a peaceful subject of the King. He also promised to become a Christian.

One sunny day, Roland and the King met on the banks of the Epte river. There, as Roland was baptized a Christian, he swore he would always be loyal to King Charles. The King gave Roland the title of Duke. When the meeting was almost over, one of King Charles's men said to Roland, "You must obey the French custom and kiss the King's foot." Roland refused, saying, "I'll never kneel before anyone or kiss anyone's foot." Again, the King's man said, "You must obey! You must kiss the King's foot." So, Roland ordered one of his men to do the deed for him. The man did as he was told. He grabbed the King's foot and lifted it to his lips, but he would not kneel down. The King fell backward out of his chair. The people who were watching burst out laughing. That was the last time the King ever ordered Roland to do anything.

After Roland became a subject of the King, he moved onto the land the King had given him. He called it Normandy and divided it among his men. Then Roland said to his men, "Any man who steals a single thing in Normandy will be hanged. This is a law you are all to obey. Also, you must promise not to fight with one another." This was a good law, because from then on there was more order in Normandy than anywhere else in France, or in Europe.

The Vikings who settled in Normandy became Christians and rebuilt all the churches they had burned. They also learned to speak French and to follow many French customs. Over the years they became less warlike and learned to live a more peaceful life. But they also kept many of their own customs, especially their codes of bravery and loyalty to one another.

So it came about that the people of Normandy were not French and they were not Viking. However, they kept the best from each of these countries. By doing so they made Normandy great!

Not only did the Vikings go to the countries of Western Europe, such as France and Germany, but they also went to lands which were farther away. Often they started in one direction, but bad storms would blow them far out into the middle of the ocean. They had no compasses to guide them. No one is certain how they found land again. An Irish legend says that the Vikings used crows as their guides.

According to the Irish legend, these bold Northern warriors carried many cages of crows with them on their ships. When a storm chanced to blow the ships any distance from land, the Vikings would set a crow free. As the crow left the cage, he would fly toward the nearest land. In turn, the Vikings would steer in the direction of the crow's flight. Thus, the legend says, by following the direction the crow flies, the Vikings never became lost even when they were in the middle of the ocean and without knowledge of directions.

Of course, no one knows whether the Vikings really used crows to find their way safely to land, but the story is part of the Viking legend! Also, from the legend comes a saying used and heard frequently today: "Follow the direction that crows fly," or "straight as the crow flies."

Regardless of whether the Vikings used crows, it is known that a storm, not crows, drove them to discover the New World. It was in the eight hundreds A.D., in the year of 861, that a Norwegian Viking ship sailed from a port in Norway. Soon after they set sail, they encountered a terrible storm. Of course, this did not frighten these bold Viking warriors. But, later, when they released a crow, they were unable to see the bird or to follow the direction because of the wind, rain, and turbulence of the sea. They could only hope that eventually they would sight land. They knew that the storm was carrying them far away from their native Norway. Of course this gave them some concern. But being brave warriors, they did not show their feelings. However, it is likely that many of them asked one another, "Where is this storm carrying us? Where will we land? Will we have to remain at sea forever, or will we find some new land?"

When the storm was finally over, the Vikings found themselves near an island which they had never seen before. They knew immediately that they were in a new world and a long distance from Norway. They were concerned and surprised to see an island completely covered with snow. Since this island was covered only with snow, they named it Snowland. Two years later, a Swedish Viking, named Gardar Svaforson made a return sailing trip to this island. He landed and spent the winter exploring the island. Then he renamed the island Iceland, and set up a Viking colony there. Within a few years, many people had followed Svaforson to Iceland, and the colony there grew quite large.

One of the Vikings who followed Svaforson to Iceland was a Norwegian named Eric the Red. He was called this because he had bright red hair. It is said that he also had a very bad temper. One day, in a temper, he killed a man. As punishment for this crime, he was forced to leave Iceland. He was also told he could not go back to Norway.

Taking some of his family and friends with him, Eric the Red sailed in search of a place to live. After sailing for many days, he found an island that was warmer than Iceland and had richer soil. He decided to settle there. He named the land, Greenland. It was summertime and all of the grass and trees were a lovely green.

Eric the Red's son, Leif Ericson, sailed with his father to Greenland. One day, in the year 999, Leif Ericson left Greenland and set sail for Norway. A very bad storm carried his ship far away to a new land where there were many wheat fields and wild vineyards. Leif soon returned to Greenland and told the people there of the land he had found. Within a short time, explorers went out from Greenland to look at the lands of which Leif spoke. The first place they landed they called Helluland, which means "lands of rocks." Historians today believe that Helluland is Labrador or Newfoundland. Going on, the Vikings came to the land that Leif Ericson had found. They named it Vinland, or Wineland, because of the wild vineyards growing there. They settled down in a part of Vinland, which was probably not too far from where New York City stands today.

After three years, the Vikings left their colony in Vinland.

The wild Indians who lived there had attacked them constantly during most of their stay. So the colonists decided to go back to their more peaceful life in Greenland. Not until five hundred years later, when Columbus sailed to the New World, did a white man set foot on American land again.

America, France, Germany, Russia, the Vikings went to all of these lands and to many more, affecting the histories of these places when they touched there. As much as any other people of these times, the Vikings helped to shape the course which the world would follow. Nothing shows the true thoughts and feelings of these "Kings of the Sea" better than the stories and legends of their deeds. These stories and legends are called "sagas." They were passed down from father to son by the Vikings, as they sat around their fires at night, drinking and preparing for the next day of battle. Everyone enjoys these legends and stories, and three are retold here: "The Vikings' Promises," "Old Sterdoker," and "The Saga of Fridtjof."

THE VIKINGS' PROMISES

Many, many years ago there was a group of Vikings who lived on an island in the middle of the Oder River. Led by their chief, Duke Sigwald, this strong, fearless group of men spent their time attacking nearby lands. Most of the lands they raided belonged to the Danish King, Svend of the Two Beards. Svend wanted very much to stop Duke Sigwald's attacks, but he did not dare to fight with him. Duke Sigwald had many more men than the King. Also, the Vikings were stronger than King Svend's people. King Svend knew he would have to get rid of the Vikings by means of some trick. Finally he thought of a plan. His first step was to invite them to a great feast which he was having in honor of his dead father, King Harold.

On the day of the feast Duke Sigwald and his men arrived in sixty dragon ships. King Svend and all the men of his court met them when they landed. They led the Vikings to huge tables which were piled high with drinks and food of all kinds. King Svend asked the Vikings to sit down with him.

All that day, and far into the night, the Vikings sat eating and drinking. They began to laugh, sing, and tell funny stories. King Svend saw that the drinks were making the Vikings act silly. They were also off guard. So he rose from his chair and said, "This feast is in honor of my father, King Harold. I ask all of you to drink to him, with me."

"To King Harold," the Vikings shouted as they drank their huge cups of mead.

Again and again King Svend asked the Vikings to drink with him in honor of his father. When he saw that they were very drunk, the King raised his arms to quiet the crowd and said, "It is the custom at feasts like this, where many great men come together, to make promises in honor of the day. I will make a promise, even though I am sure that all of you will make even better promises. I know that the Vikings are the greatest of all warriors, and that their promises have to be greater than anyone else's. But, here is my promise. I promise that before three winters pass I will drive King Ethelred of England out of his country. If I cannot make him leave England, I will kill him myself and add England to my Kingdom. Now, Duke Sigwald, it is your turn. I dare you to make a promise as good as mine."

After drinking another cup of mead, Sigwald answered King Svend. "I shall make war on Norway," he said. "Within two years I will drive King Haakon out of his country. If I cannot, I will at least die in Norway trying to do so."

"What a great promise!" cried King Svend. "But I see that your brother, Dorkel the Great, wants to make a promise too. Certainly he will say something wonderful."

Dorkel turned to King Svend and said, "I shall not leave my brother Sigwald until every man on earth has lost his shadow. As long as he fights with his enemies, I will be by his side."

The King replied, "I'm sure you are a man who will keep his promise. And you, Bue the Fat. If your promise is as big as you are, we will hear great words from you."

Bue the Fat was a man so large that it was said three men could fit into his coat quite easily. "Here is my promise, King Svend," he said. "I shall go with Duke Sigwald to Norway, and I shall stay with him until not one of our enemies is left standing."

"I thought you would say something like that," King Svend told Bue the Fat. "Now, let's hear what Sigurd has to say. Everyone says he is one of the bravest of all men. Sigurd, you have heard what your brother, Bue the Fat, has promised to do. What will you do?" asked King Svend.

"My promise is short. I shall follow my brother Bue the Fat; I shall run if he runs; I shall die if he dies," replied Sigurd.

"I knew you were as brave as your brother!" exclaimed King Svend "And you, Vagn! Your uncles, Bue the Fat and Sigurd, have made great promises. What do you have to say?"

Vagn walked to the middle of the room. He was tall and handsome and the strongest of all the Vikings. "Listen to my promise, King Svend," he said. "I shall go with Duke Sigwald to Norway. As long as he lives he will see my sword in action. But I have two more promises to make. The first is that I shall not return home without marrying Ingebord, the daughter of the Norwegian, Dorkel Lera. She is the most beautiful girl in the world, and no one will stop me from making her my wife. My second promise is that I will kill Dorkel Lera, the bravest Norwegian of them all. I care not that he is Ingebord's father."

"Ah, yes, your promise is greater than anyone else's, Vagn," said the King. "It is said far and wide that you are the bravest of all men, and your promise shows that it is so." The King then drank to Vagn.

Prodded into making good their boasts, the Vikings soon set sail for Norway, leaving King Svend at peace.

In the first ship rode Duke Sigwald. Then came Bue the Fat, then Vagn, the strongest of the Vikings. Each of them was in charge of many ships. They all had only one aim: to win the battle with Norway!

As the Vikings neared the coast of Norway, King Haakon sent out his bravest men and best ships to fight them. With their sails up and their oars out, the "dragons" of both lands ran to meet each other. The sea seemed alive with ships, and the sounds of battle filled the air. Swords crashed against shields and coats of iron! Cries of men, cut down by the terrible battle-axes, were heard on all sides! Here, a man lost an arm. There, another lost his head! The Vikings of Sigwald could not be stopped! Soon, many of the Norwegian ships carried only dead sailors in them. King Haakon's battle was lost. His men turned their remaining ships around and sailed toward their shore.

When King Haakon reached land, he knew he would need a great deal of help to win any battle with the fierce Vikings. So, he ordered his youngest son, Erlig, to come to him. King Haakon then sacrificed his son to the gods and also asked Odin for help. When this was done, he and his men went back to battle the Vikings.

Again, the Vikings seemed to be winning the battle, but all at once a storm came down upon their ships. The winds blew. Stones, arrows, and spears rained down from the clouds onto the Vikings. Suddenly the sky came to life, and Odin's men rode out of the clouds and attacked Duke Sigwald and his men.

In the meantime, King Haakon had headed his ship into the midst of the Viking dragons. The ship went so fast it seemed to be flying. As it drew nearer to them, the Vikings saw a woman standing on the deck. She raised her arms and arrows shot out from her fingers. Streams of fire came from her mouth and swords flew from her eyes. No one could be saved from this horrible witch! Some of the bravest Vikings fell before her awful attack.

When Duke Sigwald saw the witch, he was so afraid he ordered his ship out of the battle and sailed away as fast as he could go. Bue the Fat and Vagn stayed on to fight. They fought bravely, but finally Bue the Fat was very badly hurt. He would not let himself be taken prisoner. In his ship there were two boxes of gold. Holding one heavy box in each arm, Bue the Fat jumped overboard and was swallowed up by the dark waters of the sea.

Vagn fought on. He battled with the strongest and bravest of the Norwegians. After many hours, his was the only Viking ship left on the sea. All the Norwegian ships began to attack the one Viking ship. Tired from fighting, and bleeding from many cuts, Vagn was finally captured. With thirty of his men, he was taken prisoner.

That night the Norwegians had a huge feast. When they were finished eating and drinking, King Haakon spoke to them. "My friends," he said, "to please you I have decided to have the heads of all the Vikings cut off before the sun rises again. I have chosen Dorkel Lera, the bravest man in our land, and in all lands, to do this deed."

Dorkel Lera stood up and turned toward the King. "I am honored that you have chosen me to do this deed," he said. "If I show myself to be weak or afraid, may I lose all of my honor. Now, watch, and I will show you how well I use my sword."

Four of the Vikings who were very badly hurt were brought before Dorkel Lera. He raised his sword and did as he was told, killing each Viking one by one. Then turning to the king, he said proudly, "There is an old saga which says no man can cut off four heads in a row without his face changing color. Is that so?"

"Your face did not change color while you were doing the deed, but it seemed to me that you looked pale before you started," the king replied. Then he ordered another Viking to be brought before Dorkel Lera. This Viking was also very badly hurt and bloody. He could hardly move.

"You have known that you were going to die very soon, my friend," Dorkel Lera said to the Viking. "What have you been thinking about while you were waiting for my sword?"

The Viking answered, "I have been thinking about my father's death. He died by the sword also. So did my grandfather, and so did all the men in my family. It is the best way for me to die also.

Dorkel Lera raised his sword high over the man's neck and let it fall. The fifth Viking was dead, and soon another one was dragged before him. "Aren't you afraid to die?" Dorkel Lera asked.

"You should know that the Viking code does not allow fear or tears," the man replied.

"You obey your Viking code very well," said Dorkel Lera before he put an end to the Viking's life. As soon as he had done this deed, a seventh Viking was brought before him. Again Dorkel Lera asked the question, "Aren't you sorry that you are about to die?"

The Viking looked Dorkel Lera straight in the eye. He was an old man, and his body showed signs of having been in many battles. "It is better to die the way I am going to die than to live like you do. You kill men who are in chains, men who cannot fight back," he said. "You are a weak man and a coward!"

Again Dorkel Lera's sword did its work, and still another Viking was brought before him. This Viking was a young boy who had beautiful long blond hair. Dorkel Lera asked him, "Aren't you sad you are going to leave the world so soon?"

"No!" the young man answered, "I have fought beside my friends and so the best part of my life is over. I have just seen some brave Viking soldiers die. The only thing I'm sorry about is that I have lived longer than they did. All I ask now is that you have one of your men hold my hair out of the way of your sword so that no blood will get on it.

A Norwegian sailor stepped up to the Viking and grasped his hair. It was so long that he had to wrap it around his hand several times. When he had done this, he pulled the boy forward by his hair. At the same moment that Dorkel Lera's sword came down, the Viking pulled back suddenly. The sword missed the boy and cut off the Norwegian's arm. The Viking boy jumped up, shouting, "Has someone here left his hand in my hair?"

King Haakon turned to Dorkel Lera and said, "Hurry and kill the rest of the Vikings. If you do not, another Viking might trick us again!"

Before Dorkel Lera could do as King Haakon had told him, the King's eldest son, Eric, spoke up, "Wait, Dorkel Lera!" he said. Then he turned to his father and asked, "Why does this killing have to go on? These men are brave and clever. We can use fighters such as these. We should make them our subjects instead of killing them. Let's talk to them and find out something about them and their families." Turning to the young Viking who had tricked them, Eric asked him his name.

"My name is Svend. I am the son of Bue the Fat," answered the boy.

"How old are you?" Eric asked.

"I will be eighteen years old next winter, if I live," replied the boy.

"Don't worry, you will live," said Eric. "I give you my word that you will live!"

King Haakon was very angry at Eric. "All right," he said. "This man belongs to you. Now let Dorkel Lera finish his job."

"Not yet," replied Eric. "I want to speak with every one of these men and decide what will happen to each of them."

King Haakon did not say anything more. His son had a mind of his own. He usually did as he pleased. The King did not want to make Eric obey him. He wanted his son to be a strong-willed man. Someday Eric would rule Norway and he would remain king only as long as he was strong enough to lead, to fight others, and to keep the crown for himself.

Another Viking who was tall and noble, and very handsome, was brought before Eric. "And you, Viking, now that you are about to die, aren't you sorry about anything?" Eric asked.

"I am sorry about nothing except not being able to keep a promise I made," the Viking said.

"What is your name?" asked Eric. "And what is the promise that you made?"

"I am Vagn, the son of Vage. I promised that I would kill Dorkel Lera and marry his beautiful daughter, Ingebord. If I die without keeping that promise, my whole life will have been useless."

"I will stop you from keeping your promise!" shouted Dorkel Lera. He ran toward Vagn with his sword in his hand. Just as he was about to cut him down, Vagn stepped out of the way. Dorkel Lera tripped and fell forward, and his sword fell from his hand. Before the Norwegian could get to his feet again, Vagn grabbed the sword. With one quick blow he finished Dorkel Lera. "At least I have kept part of my promise," Vagn said. "Now I will die a happier man!"

King Haakon rose out of his chair and shouted to his men, "Kill him! Kill him!"

But before any of the men could make a move, Eric stepped in front of Vagn. "If you do not let me speak, you will have to kill me before you can put a hand on this Viking."

The King became very pale. He saw that Eric meant what he said. "We shall not fight over such a small thing, my son," he told Eric. "You may do with him as you wish."

"Sire, one day you will thank me for saving this man's life," said Eric. "As for Dorkel Lera, you shouldn't be surprised that he died. Just a little while ago you yourself said that he turned pale before beheading the Vikings. Everyone knows the saying that if a man's face changes color when he is going to kill someone, it is a sign that he will soon die himself."

That night when the feast was over, Eric rode back to his palace. By his side rode Vagn, and on that very night the Viking married Ingebord, the most beautiful girl in Norway. This is the end of the first story!

OLD STERDOKER

The second saga is that of Old Sterdoker. There has never been a man like Old Sterdoker. It was said that he came from the land where giants lived. It was also said that he had been born with three pairs of arms and three pairs of legs.

One day Odin, who was jealous of Sterdoker because he was so strong, tore off two of his arms and two of his legs. That left him with one pair of arms and one pair of legs. That was how Sterdoker came to look like everyone else! However, he remained very tall and very brave. In his lifetime he had fought and beaten many men who had not been beaten by anyone else.

For many long years Sterdoker sailed the sea. He had visited many lands and had fought many battles. He had many exciting adventures. But when he became old, he decided he wanted to rest. So he sailed to Denmark and went to the court of King Frode. There he said to the King, "I am Sterdoker. I am old now and want to rest. Give me a piece of land an I will rule it for you."

King Frode answered, "I do not have any land big enough for the great Sterdoker. Stay here and be the teacher for my son Ingiald and my daughter Helga."

So, Sterdoker decided to stay with the King of Denmark. He had not been there very long when King Frode was killed by some of his enemies. Ingiald then became King. Ingiald was not at all like his father. He liked to spend his time with fools, jokers, and horn players, not with soldiers and wise men. Sterdoker became very worried. One day he went to Ingiald and said, "What have you done for your people since you became King? What battles have you fought? What lands have you won? What have you done to the men who killed your father? Show me your wounds. Tell me about the enemies you have killed. Ingiald, the poets who sang about the bravery of your father will never even say your name! Your grandchildren will never know that Ingiald was King of Denmark." Having said all this to Ingiald, Sterdoker left the Court of Denmark and sailed to Sweden.

Many years passed. Helga, Ingiald's sister, became old enough to be married. Many men had asked for her hand in marriage. Among them was a Norwegian named Hroar. He was a good, brave young man, as well as being very handsome and very rich

"Hroar, I would gladly give you my sister Helga," Ingiald told him. "But others have asked for her too. You cannot have her unless you fight with every man who asks you to fight for her hand."

"I am ready for anyone who dares me to battle," Hroar answered.

As soon as Hroar had finished talking to the King, a man named Aslak spoke out. Aslak had eight brothers. His family was the meanest and strongest in Denmark. Aslak had asked Helga to marry him, but she had refused him. He was very angry when he spoke to the King. "King Ingiald," he said, "in my name and in the names of my brothers, I dare this Norwegian to fight us. If he would like, we can fight right now."

"No," Ingiald answered. "I have chosen the day for the fight. I have decided that Helga will marry Hroar. On the day after the wedding you will have your battle."

Plans for the wedding were begun. It was to be a big and beautiful wedding. A huge feast was to be held after the wedding. As the wedding day grew nearer, everyone seemed to be happy and excited. Only Hroar and Helga were very sad.

"Ah, my love," said Hroar, "what will become of you after the wedding? Will you be left alone in the world? I'm not afraid of any man, even if he is bigger than I, but how can I beat nine strong men?"

"They will surely kill you unless you listen to me and follow my plan," said Helga. "There is only one man who can help you. He is Sterdoker. You must go to Sweden to see him. If you tell him I sent you, he will be glad to help you."

Hroar set sail for Sweden at once. When he landed there, he quickly went to Sterdoker's house. He found the old man sitting in the sun with his sword Skun by his side. Hroar walked up to him and said, "Brave Viking, I am the man who is going to marry Helga, King Frode's daughter. You must know that I did not come all this way just to ask you to the wedding. I have come to ask you for help. I need you with me on the battlefield, with your sword in your hand, your helmet on your head, and your shield on your arm." Hroar then explained to Sterdoker how Aslak and his brothers had challenged him to fight them.

Sterdoker listened to Hroar's story without saying a word. When Hroar had finished, he only asked, "What day? Where?" After Hroar had answered his questions, the old man said, "All right. Go home and wait."

Hroar returned to Denmark. Soon, the wedding day arrived, but there was no sign of Sterdoker. At the feast, after the wedding, Aslak and his brothers joked in loud voices about the battle to be held the next day. They said to Hroar, "Eat and drink as much as you can, Norwegian, because you'll need all the strength you have to face each of us. Tomorrow, when the sun comes up, we will wait for you on the Roliung Plains. It is quiet there and no one will bother us."

Hroar pretended to laugh. He said, "You had better have a good time here today. Tomorrow you may be surprised! I will not be alone."

Aslak and his brothers thought that Hroar was not telling the truth. They were not worried by what he said. Since Sterdoker had not yet arrived, Hroar began to wonder if, after all, he would be alone in battle the next day.

When the feast was almost over, Sterdoker walked into the room. He made his way between the tables. He pushed aside anyone who stood in his path. Without a word he sat down at the table of honor next to Helga.

Many people in the hall knew Sterdoker. They were too afraid of him to tell him that they were angry with him. But, the nine brothers began to shout at Sterdoker. He turned to them and said, "I think I hear dogs barking. Eh! try to keep quiet!"

"Who is this crazy old man?" shouted Aslak. "What is he doing? He should be punished for coming here."

Sterdoker looked at Aslak and said, "How many of you are there? Nine brave and strong boys, I hear. Well, it's too bad there are not more of you because I would gladly fight with as many of you as would dare face me."

When Sterdoker had finished speaking, Aslak and his brothers knew that he was the man Hroar had said would help him. After that, they sat down and thought again about the battle on the next day.

Later that night Hroar and Helga went to their home. Sterdoker followed behind them. When they reached the door of their house they turned to Sterdoker and asked, "Where are you going to spend the night?" Without answering their question, he followed them into the house and closed the door. Then he put his coat down in front of the door. He lay down on it and immediately went to sleep.

A short time later, Hroar awoke. He went to the window and opened it. He looked out. It was still night, and the air was so still that he went back to sleep.

With the first light of the new day, Sterdoker woke up and waited for Hroar to call him. He waited and waited. Finally he pushed open the door to the bedroom and looked in. Hroar and Helga were still asleep. He was very angry with Hroar, but he said to himself, "Why should I bother them? Sterdoker will not awaken anyone who does not get up in time for battle, nor will he let anyone think he was too afraid to go and fight alone!"

The old man left the palace. It was a bitterly cold morning with snow over all the land. As Sterdoker walked to the Roliung Plains he began to think, "How silly young people are today. One man is still asleep and the other men probably will not dare to leave their house on such a cold day!"

When Sterdoker got to the Roliung Plains, he took off all his clothes. He threw his coat over a bush and then sat down in the snow to wait.

Aslak and his brothers took a different path to the Plains. When they arrived they sat behind a hill to avoid the cold wind.

They built a fire to help warm themselves. As time passed, Aslak said to one of his brothers, "Climb the hill and see if you can find anyone there."

The brother went up the hill. When he returned, he said to Aslak, "I have seen a very strange thing.

"There is an old man sitting in the snow without any clothes. His coat is spread out over a bush, and he is facing into the cold north wind."

The brothers went to see this strange sight. As they got nearer to the man, they saw that it was Sterdoker. Going up to him, Aslak said, "Old man, we do not want to be unfair to you. We will fight with you one at a time."

Sterdoker got up and dressed again. Then he said, "You are dogs. I shall beat all of you at once."

Angrily, the brothers took out their swords and stood in a circle around Sterdoker. They raised their shields and began attacking him from all sides. It was a cruel battle. Shields were broken, helmets were torn, and blood fell on the snow in showers. Soon six bodies lay side by side on the ground.

Although Old Sterdoker was not hurt, he was out of breath. When he stopped to rest, the three brothers who were left attacked him like wild animals. Slash! Slash! Slash! At the same time Sterdoker's sword Skun cut into arms, legs, and heads. Soon, only Aslak was alive to fight with Sterdoker. With one quick blow the old man hit Aslak so hard that he was dead, almost at once!

Now that the battle was over, Sterdoker saw that he was hurt. Blood flowed from seventeen cuts on his body. Using the last bit of strength he had, Sterdoker crawled to a rock. Here he fell down. He was very, very, very tired.

Luckily a farmer in a cart passed by and saw Sterdoker lying on the rock. He ran to him and cleaned his cuts with snow. Then the farmer gave Sterdoker some water. The farmer lifted

Sterdoker onto his cart and started toward King Ingiald's palace.

In the meantime, Hroar had awakened. The morning was almost over, and Sterdoker was nowhere to be found. "Oh, what kind of a man am I!" cried Hroar. "I slept instead of fighting! How can I face Sterdoker if he comes back? What will I do if he has been killed?

"Hroar, Sterdoker will win the fight with or without you," Helga said. But when he returns he will be very angry that you slept throughout the battle. Don't cry and don't show him that you are afraid of him. You must fight bravely with him because he likes brave men as much as he hates cowardly ones."

Helga was right when she said Sterdoker would be very angry when he returned to the palace. As soon as the cart in which he was riding came near the palace, Sterdoker jumped off. With his sword Skun in his hand, he ran toward the palace gate, shouting, "Where is the boy who sleeps while a man fights his battles for him? Let me see him. I will teach him to be *a man!*"

Three of the palace guards ran toward Sterdoker. They tried to keep him out of the palace. With three sharp blows he knocked them to the ground. The guards at the gate also tried to stop Sterdoker, but they were no match for him. His anger drove him on. Into the courtyard and up the stairs he went. At each step men came from all sides to stop him. But no one could stop Sterdoker! With his sword Skun he ran through the palace like a terrible storm, the kind of storm that comes very suddenly and reaches out to cut down anything that stands in its way!

Finally, he reached Hroar's bedroom. He ran to the door and kicked it down. Hroar was waiting for him with his sword in his hand. When the old man attacked him, Hroar hit Sterdoker so hard that he knocked the sword out of his hand. Before the old man could pick up his sword, Hroar hit him again. With his

second blow, Hroar split
Sterdoker's shield in two
parts and then he buried his
own sword deep into the floor.

"Aha!" cried Sterdoker.
"I see that you would have
done well in the battle today
if you had been there. Helga
is yours. You have won her."

For many years Sterdoker
stayed with Helga and
Hroar. The older he got, the
more unhappy he became.
"Why can't I die like a
soldier? Is there no man who
will send me to Odin's palace?" he would cry. But
everyone knew that even
though he was old, Ster-
doker was still very strong.
No one dared to attack him.

One day he decided to go
in search of the man who
would fight him to the death.
He put his gold in a sack
and hung it around his neck.
He took his sword Skun and
went off on his crutches.
From city to city and from
land to land he went. But
no one would dare to fight
with him.

Then one day, while Sterdoker was crossing the Roliung Plains, he saw a group of men on horses coming towards him. They were riding very fast. They were taking up all of the road. Sterdoker made no move to get out of their way. Instead he kept right on going, with his crutches.

"How brave that beggar is!" said their leader. "Ride your horses toward him and run him out of our way."

Three of the men rode toward Sterdoker as fast as they could. When they got to the old man, he swung his crutches at the riders, knocking them off their horses.

The young leader was very surprised and asked, "Who are you, old man?" You can do more with your crutches than most men can do with a sword."

Sterdoker answered, "I am too old and you are too young for us to have met. Some of the older men in your family may know me. My name is Sterdoker."

"Sterdoker!" said the young man. "There is no man on earth who does not know who you are. I am Hader, the son of Hlenes."

"Ah, Hader, many years ago your father and I were friends," said Sterdoker. "I should have known who you were right away. You look just like your father."

Sterdoker went on, "The last time I saw your father we had a very good fight. I smashed his head to pieces with my sword Skun."

Hader became very pale. "Be quiet, or I will forget you are an old man," he said.

"Ah, you get angry as any good son should. But you also should not attack me because I am an old, sick man. You are a true Viking. I like you, and I, who never have asked a favor of anyone, will now ask a favor of you. I am very old now and for a long time I have wanted to die. Sterdoker must not die in bed like a dog. I must die like a soldier, but no one will help me.

You are my last chance. If you will kill me, I shall go to Valhalla and be happy. And you will make the spirit of your father happy, too, by killing the man who killed him."

When Sterdoker had finished speaking, Hader said, "I will do what you ask."

He climbed down from his horse and walked over to Sterdoker. When he started to reach for his sword, the old man raised his hand to stop him.

"Wait!" he said. "If any sword can kill Sterdoker it is my great sword Skun. It is only right that I should die by the sword that has killed so many brave warriors."

Sterdoker handed Skun to Hader, saying, "Hold the sword very tightly. When I put my head down, hit my neck hard. You must not be afraid! You must swing at me as hard as you can. You must be sure to kill me at once."

"Because you are doing me this favor, I will tell you a secret. If you can jump between my body and my head before my head touches the ground, all of my strength that I have had in life will be yours. Your life will be as great as mine has been. No man will be able to beat you!"

Sterdoker bowed his head. Hader raised the great sword Skun high over the old Viking's neck and brought it down as hard as he could. The deed was done. The old, brave warrior was dead. However, Hader knew that it was not safe to trust the clever man whose name he had heard since he was a small child. It was true that the old man had asked to be killed, but it was not likely that he would let anyone kill him without his trying to get even. So Hader did not try to jump between Sterdoker's head and his body. He thought that perhaps the Viking had planned to kill him by squashing him under his huge body as he died.

Hader and his men buried Sterdoker on the Roliung Plains. This was the place where he had fought many times and where he had died. They marked his grave with a huge pile of rocks. Now, everyone who saw it would know it was the grave of a great and brave man. Then taking Sterdoker's sword and his gold, Hader rode away.

As they were crossing the Roliung bridge, Hader dropped Sterdoker's sword Skun into the deep waters of the river. Since that day, many men have tried to get Skun for themselves. When they reach for it, all they find in their hand is a pile of sand. It is said that the sword will lie shining at the bottom of the river until a man as brave as Sterdoker comes for it!

THE SAGA OF FRIDTJOF

The third story takes place in the "Land of Song." Here, there once lived a man named Fridtjof. He was young, strong, and said by all to be one of the wisest and bravest men in the Northland. He was also very rich. Of all his possessions, there were two which Fridtjof loved more than any of the others. The first was his ship *Ellida*, which was very beautiful and very fast. The second was a gold arm band. This was so beautiful that there was not another one in the world which could match it.

Fridtjof ruled part of the "Land of Song." He was a subject of both King Helge and King Halfdan, who were brothers. Helge and Halfdan were the same age as Fridtjof. But they were not as clever or as strong as he was. Day by day, they watched as Fridtjof grew richer and they grew poorer. They were very jealous of Fridtjof, and the richer he became, the less they liked him.

The two kings had a beautiful sister named Ingebord. She was in love with Fridtjof. The two brothers were angry at her because of her love for him. They would say to each other, "Our sister cannot love him just for his riches. She cannot love him for himself, either. So he must have tricked her into falling in love with him by telling her many falsehoods."

One day Fridtjof went to the palace to see Helge and Halfdan. "Sirs, I love your sister Ingebord the Beautiful," he told them. "I have come to ask you for her hand in marriage."

The two brothers answered him angrily. They said, "The sister of Kings is too good for a subject. She does not love you, and you cannot have her."

When the Kings had finished answering Fridtjof, he said to them, "My visit is over. But let me tell you this. From now on you will not be welcome in my house. You will never get any help from me!"

Now it just so happened that at this same time there was a King named Ring, who ruled the land of Ringerike. He was a warlike man who spent much of his time attacking other lands. When he heard that Fridtjof was no longer loyal to Helge and Halfdan, he decided to take advantage of their weakness. He sent them a message telling them that if they did not give him ten thousand gold coins, he would attack them and take away their lands.

When Helga and Halfdan got Ring's message, they gathered their men together. But before they could go into battle, they knew they first had to attend to an important matter. They knew that while they were away fighting, Fridtjof would try to see Ingebord. The brothers could not leave her alone in the palace. So they finally decided to take her to Baldershage. This was a holy place where the Gods of the North were honored. It was a place where she could find peace and quiet. In Baldershage the men and the women were not allowed to speak to one another. Here, it was also forbidden to kill any animals. Even the wildest were safe here. So, the Kings knew their sister would be safe in this place.

As soon as the Kings had taken their sister to Baldershage and they had gone away to fight with King Ring, Fridtjof decided to go after Ingebord. He put on his best clothes and his gold arm band. Then he set sail for the holy place on his ship *Ellida*.

When Ingebord saw Fridtjof landing at Baldershage, she cried out, "Are you mad, Fridtjof? You will make the gods very angry!"

"My love for you is greater than the anger of the gods," Fridtjof replied.

Ingebord quickly lost her fear. She also forgot about the anger of the gods and asked Fridtjof and his men to stay at Baldershage.

When the time came for Fridtjof to leave Baldershage, Ingebord said to him, "My dear, you are wearing the most beautiful armband in the world. Wouldn't it look better on a woman's arm?"

"Ingebord, it shall be yours if you promise not to take it off until the day when you no longer love me. Give me yours. We will trade armbands as a sign that we love only one another."

While Fridtjof was with Ingebord, Helge and Halfdan had met Ring's army. It was very large. Upon seeing it, the Kings had decided they did not have enough men to fight. They sent a message to Ring asking him for peace.

"If you will accept me as your ruler and give me your sister Ingebord for my wife, I will give you peace," Ring told them.

The Kings had no choice but to agree. They went to Balder-shage to get Ingebord for Ring. When they learned that Fridtjof had visited her, they were very angry. They knew they could not beat Fridtjof in a fight because he was stronger than they. So, they thought of a clever plan to punish him. They sent him a message, saying, "We have learned that you went to Balder-shage. Because we do not believe in fighting with our own people, we shall not attack you. But as a punishment for offending the gods, you must sail to the Orkney Islands. There you must get the money that the people of this island have owed us for many years."

Fridtjof answered the Kings, saying, "I want peace between us, so I will do as you have ordered me. But you must promise that while I am gone my lands and my people will be safe."

Helge and Halfdan promised Fridtjof that they would protect his lands. Quickly, Fridtjof set sail for the Orkney Islands. As soon as he had left, the two Kings attacked his land, burning down his houses and killing his people. Then they went to see two witches, Heida and Hamgliaana. "Fridtjof is sailing toward the Orkney Islands in his ship *Ellida*," they told the witches. "If you will use your black magic to stir up a storm that will sink his ship, we will give you anything in our kingdom that you want."

The witches agreed to help the Kings. They quickly filled a pot with toads and bird wings. They started their magic! They rolled their eyes and let out horrible cries. Soon smoke began to rise from the pot, and out on the ocean a terrible storm broke.

On the ocean, Fridtjof and his men saw the storm coming. Suddenly, there were huge waves as far as the eye could see. But the *Ellida* sailed on. Soon rain began to fall and then snow. A dark cloud covered the ship, and water poured into the "dragon" from all sides. Four men were washed overboard and disappeared in the dark waters.

"If we have to die, I am ready," said Fridtjof's brother, Bjorn. But I still have hope. If it were not so dark, we could see how close to land we are. Fridtjof, climb the mast and look around."

Fridtjof went up the mast. When he came back down again, he said, "There is a big dogfish swimming in circles around us. There are also two old women on its back. My friends, I think that the Kings have attacked us with magic. This bad storm is the work of those witches. Let us see which is stronger, my good luck or their witchcraft. Row toward them and give me my strongest sword."

Fridtjof stood in the front part of the dragon ship as the *Ellida* sailed toward the witches. With his sword, he put an end to them.

Down to the bottom of the sea went the two witches!

Suddenly, the storm was over! The *Ellida* sailed on. When Fridtjof returned to his home, he found his lands were ruined. He decided to get even with the two Kings. He learned that they were in Baldershage. So, he took all his men and sailed to the holy place. He was in a deep anger with the Kings because of their broken promises.

Landing at Baldershage, Fridtjof and his men found the ships which had carried the Kings there. "Take your axes and smash holes in all these ships." Fridtjof ordered his men. Then he went to the Kings' house alone.

Fridtjof found the Kings drinking and offering animals to the gods as a sacrifice. He walked right up to King Helge and said, "King, here is the gold from the Orkney Islands." And without another word, he threw the sack of gold into the King's face. The King was knocked out of his chair, flat on his back. When Fridtjof saw that Helge wore the arm band he had given Ingebord, he snatched it off the King's arm. Then reaching into a nearby fire, he picked out a burning stick and threw it against the roof. At once the house caught fire and everyone ran out in fear!

In the panic caused by the fire, Fridtjof slipped away. When Helge saw what had happened, he called to some of his men, "Catch Fridtjof and kill him!" The soldiers tried to go after Fridtjof in their boats. But when they tried to set sail, water poured into their boats from the holes which Fridtjof's men had made. They had to turn back, and Fridtjof sailed safely away.

"What will you do now?" asked Bjorn. You can't go home. You have burned down a holy place."

"I will go far away from here to battle with other people in other lands," said Fridtjof. And for several years he sailed from island to island, from coast to coast. Each year his fame grew and so did his riches. Many great men joined his group. Before long the name of Fridtjof, the Brave, was known and honored in

all the northern lands. But fame and fortune did not seem to mean much to Fridtjof. As the years passed he became more and more unhappy.

One day he suddenly said to Bjorn, "I am tired of going from one land to another. My heart is in Norway and I must go back there. I shall never be happy until I have killed the man who married Ingebord. She is the only girl I ever loved." So that very day Fridtjof's friends left him on the coast of Ringerike. Without turning back even once for a last look at his ship, Fridtjof started walking to the castle where the King and his Queen lived.

When Fridtjof reached the castle, he went into the large room where the King and Queen sat. He wore a dirty, torn coat and was bent over like an old man. He went quietly to a chair and sat down. He didn't want anyone to know that he was in the room. So he sat close to the door. However, the King had very good eyes. He had seen Fridtjof enter. He turned quickly to Ingebord and said, "An old man just walked into the room. Even though he is bent over, he seems taller and more grand than any of my men. I must talk to him and find out who he is."

Ring sent a man over to Fridtjof. The man said, "The King wants to talk with you."

"I will go with you," said Fridtjof.

When Fridtjof faced the King, Ring asked, "Who are you, traveler?"

Fridtjof replied, "My name is Thief. I have come from the land of dreams to stay in the house of the Wolf."

The King did not understand Fridtjof's answer, but he was very interested in him. "Take off your coat, sir, and sit down by my side," said the King.

When Fridtjof took off his coat, everyone was surprised at his clothes. He was dressed in blue and had a beautiful gold arm band shining on his arm. A bag full of gold hung at his waist.

"Your coat does not go with your clothes," said the King. "I will have the Queen give you a better one." So Ring sent the Queen to bring a handsome coat for the stranger.

"I'll do whatever you ask," the Queen told Ring, "but this man makes me very uneasy." However, she found a red cloak and put it over Fridtjof's shoulders. Suddenly, she saw the arm band he was wearing. She became very pale! But she did not say a word.

The King and Fridtjof talked for many hours. Finally, the King said, "I have never seen a beggar dressed as you or who is as interesting as you are. I would like you to stay here with me for as long as you like."

For over a year Fridtjof stayed with King Ring. Everyone at the Palace was very kind to him and he was welcome everywhere. Only the Queen would not talk with him.

One day the King took Fridtjof walking in the woods with him. They were so busy talking that they did not notice where they were going. They became lost. In fact, the King became so tired he decided to take a nap.

"But, sir," warned Fridtjof, "it is foolish for a King to sleep outside the palace without his faithful guards beside him."

"I am so tired that I don't care!" said Ring.

As Fridtjof sat beside the sleeping King a great struggle went on within him. He felt fear and love, hate and friendship, for the King. Finally he took out his sword and raised it over the King. But he could not use it! So he threw the sword into the bushes.

A short time later, King Ring awakened and smiled at Fridtjof. Calling him by his real name, the King said, "Fridtjof, I have known who you are from the day you walked into my home. You could have killed me, but you are a noble man. The good in you is strong. Now I want to honor you as you should be honored."

"You can do nothing more for me than you already have done," said Fridtjof. "Now, I must return to my friends."

"Don't leave me, Fridtjof," said the King. "I love you more than any other man. I shall reward you beyond all your dreams. I do not have many days left on this earth. When I die, you shall marry Ingebord. My riches will be yours and you will rule this land."

A short time later the King died. Soon after, Fridtjof married Ingebord and became the King of Ringerike. And here ends "The Saga of Fridtjof"!